KT-501-899

THIS WHERE'S WALLY? BOOK BELONGS TO:

HEY, WALLY FANS! FIVE INTREPID TRAVELLERS
ARE LOST IN EVERY SCENE! CAN YOU FIND THEM?

ODLAW   WIZARD
WHITEBEARD   WENDA   WOOF   WALLY

AND IN EVERY SCENE, THE TRAVELLERS
HAVE EACH LOST SOMETHING PRECIOUS!
CAN YOU FIND THEM TOO?

WALLY'S KEY   WOOF'S BONE   WENDA'S CAMERA

WIZARD WHITEBEARD'S SCROLL   ODLAW'S BINOCULARS

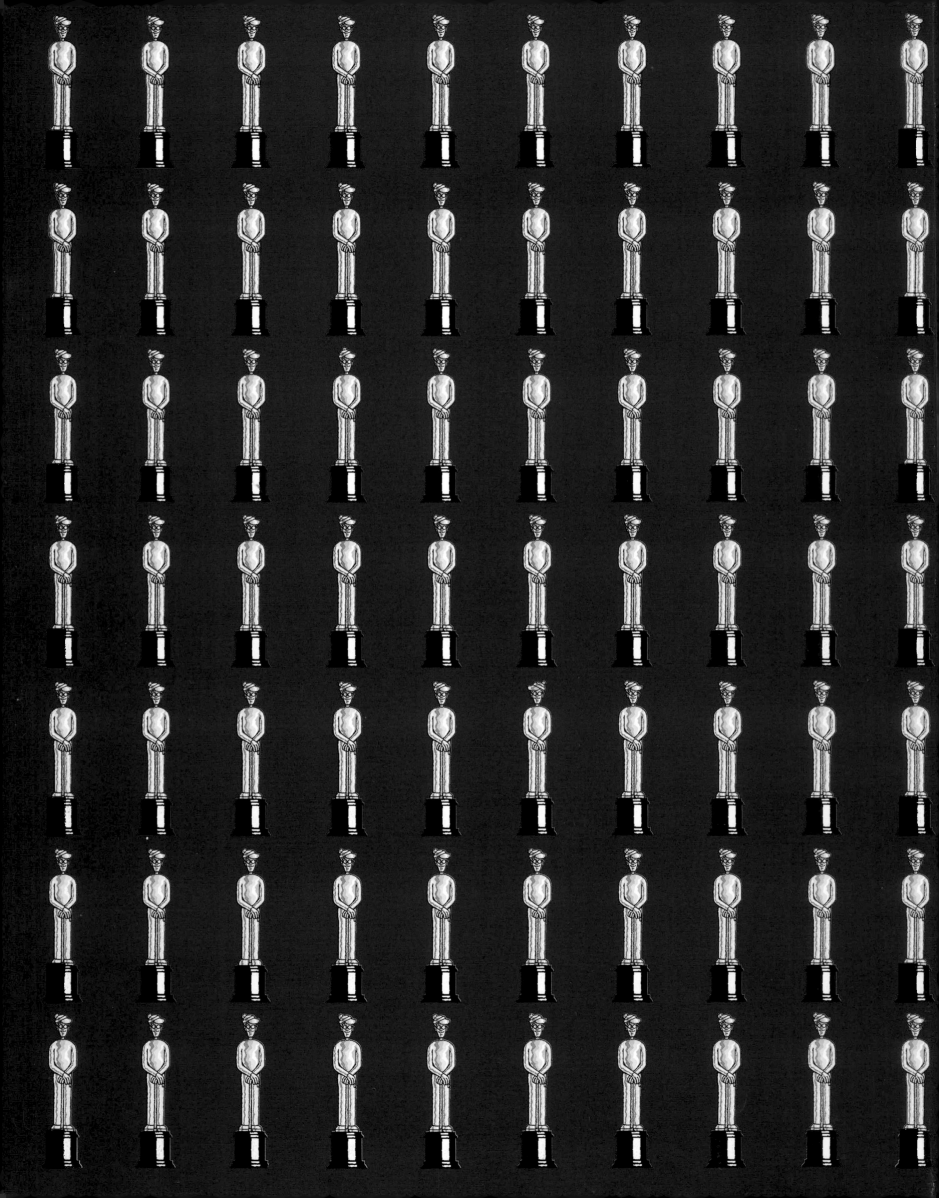

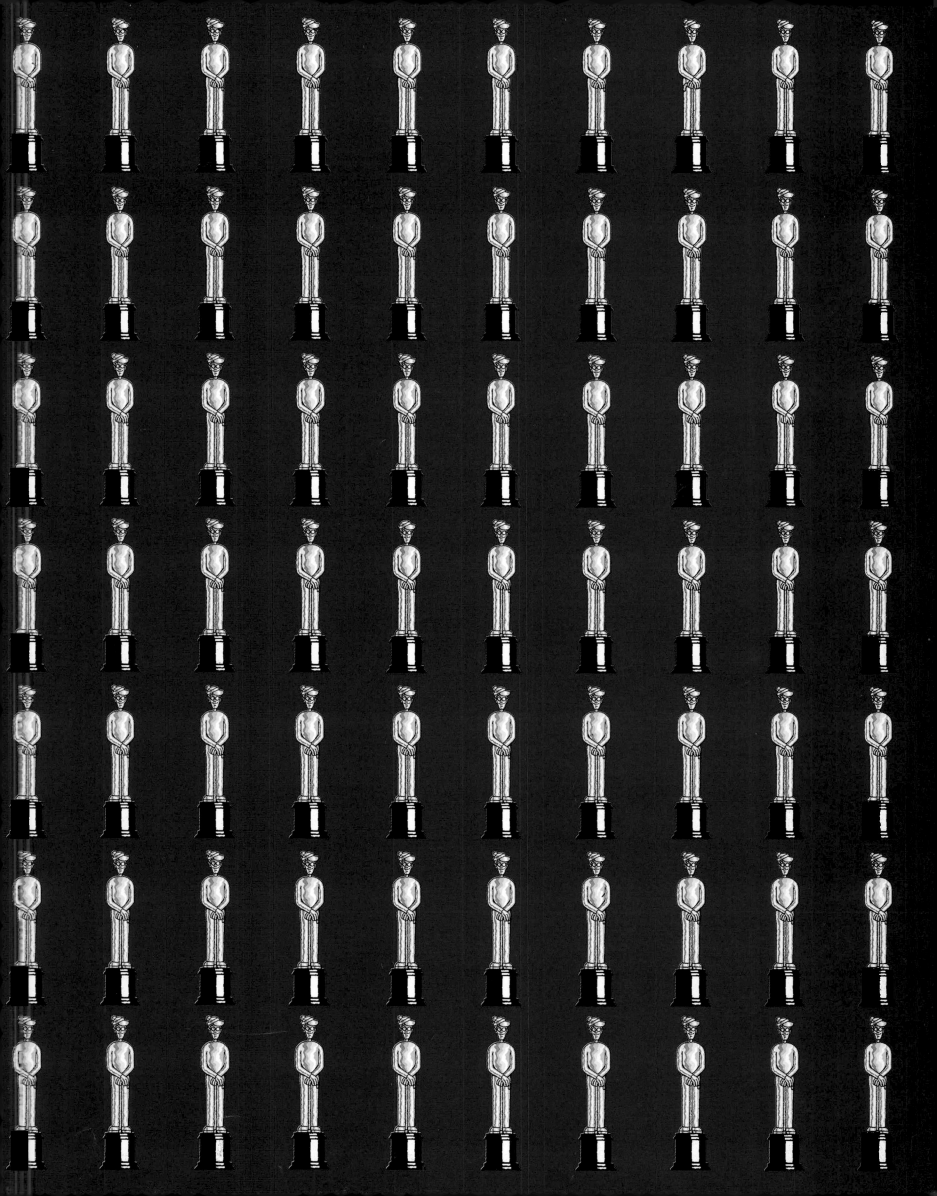

TO ELIZABETH, MIKE,
STEVE, EDDY AND TERRY
FOR ALL THEIR HELP
AND ENCOURAGEMENT

First published 1993 by Walker Books Ltd
87 Vauxhall Walk, London SE11 5HJ
This edition published 2014

2 4 6 8 10 9 7 5 3 1

© 1993, 1997, 2007, 2014 Martin Handford

The right of Martin Handford to be identified as author/illustrator of this work has been
asserted by him in accordance with the Copyright, Designs and Patents Act 1988.
Use of the Hollywood sign ™/© 1993 Hollywood Chamber of Commerce under license
authorized by Curtis Management Group, Indianapolis, Indiana, USA
King Kong © 1993 RKO Pictures, Inc. All rights reserved. Courtesy of Turner Entertainment Co.

This book has been typeset in Wallyfont and Optima.   •   Printed in China   •   All rights reserved.

British Library Cataloguing in Publication Data:
a catalogue record for this book is available from the British Library.

Part of a pack: ISBN 978-1-4063-6109-4
This edition is part of a pack; not for resale separately.
ISBN 978-1-4063-6119-3

www.walker.co.uk

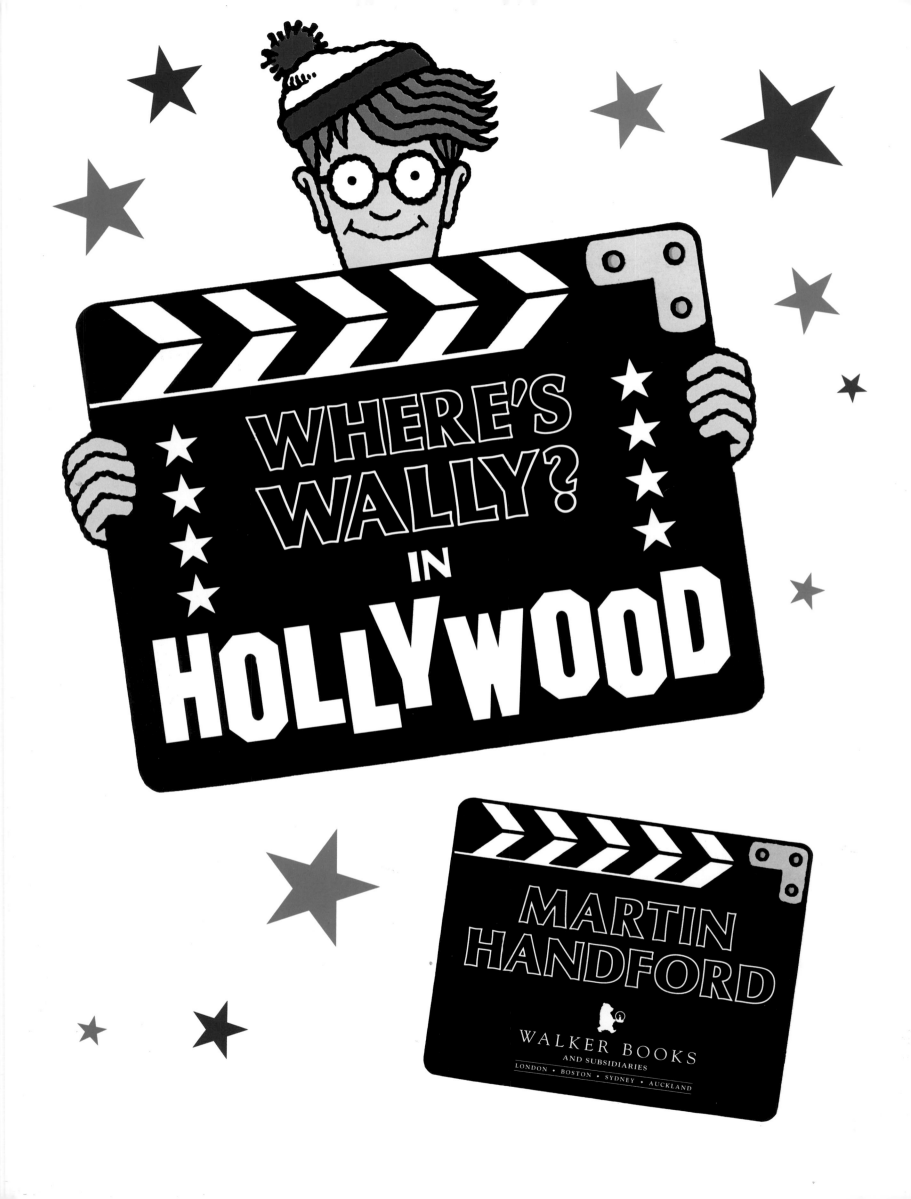

WHERE'S WALLY? IN HOLLYWOOD

MARTIN HANDFORD

WALKER BOOKS
AND SUBSIDIARIES
LONDON · BOSTON · SYDNEY · AUCKLAND

A DREAM COME TRUE

WOW, WALLY-WATCHERS, THIS IS FANTASTIC, I'M REALLY IN HOLLYWOOD! LOOK AT THE FILM PEOPLE EVERYWHERE – I WONDER WHAT MOVIES THEY'RE MAKING. THIS IS MY DREAM COME TRUE ... TO MEET THE DIRECTORS AND ACTORS, TO WALK THROUGH THE CROWDS OF EXTRAS, TO SEE BEHIND THE SCENES! PHEW, I WONDER IF I'LL APPEAR IN A MOVIE MYSELF!

★ ★ ★ ★ WHAT TO LOOK FOR IN HOLLYWOOD! ★ ★ ★ ★

WELCOME TO TINSELTOWN, WALLY-WATCHERS! THESE ARE THE PEOPLE AND THINGS TO LOOK FOR AS YOU WALK THROUGH THE FILM SETS WITH WALLY.

★ FIRST (OF COURSE!) WHERE'S WALLY?

★ NEXT FIND WALLY'S CANINE COMPANION, WOOF – REMEMBER, ALL YOU CAN SEE IS HIS TAIL!

★ THEN FIND WALLY'S FRIEND, WENDA!

★ ABRACADABRA! NOW FOCUS IN ON WIZARD WHITEBEARD!

★ BOO! HISS! HERE COMES THE BAD GUY, ODLAW!

★ NOW SPOT THESE 25 WALLY-WATCHERS, EACH OF WHOM APPEARS ONLY ONCE BEFORE THE FINAL FANTASTIC SCENE!

★ WOW! INCREDIBLE! SPOT ONE OTHER CHARACTER WHO APPEARS IN EVERY SCENE EXCEPT THE LAST!

★ ★ KEEP ON SEARCHING! THERE'S MORE TO FIND! ★ ★

ON EVERY SET FIND WALLY'S LOST KEY!

WOOF'S LOST BONE! WENDA'S LOST CAMERA! WIZARD WHITEBEARD'S SCROLL! ODLAW'S LOST BINOCULARS! AND A MISSING CAN OF FILM!

★ ★ ★ ★ ★ ★ AND MORE AND MORE! ★ ★ ★ ★ ★ ★ ★

EACH OF THE FOUR POSTERS ON THE WALL OVER THERE IS PART OF ONE OF THE FILM SETS WALLY IS ABOUT TO VISIT. ★ FIND OUT WHERE THE POSTERS CAME FROM. ★ THEN SPOT ANY DIFFERENCES BETWEEN THE POSTERS AND THE SETS.

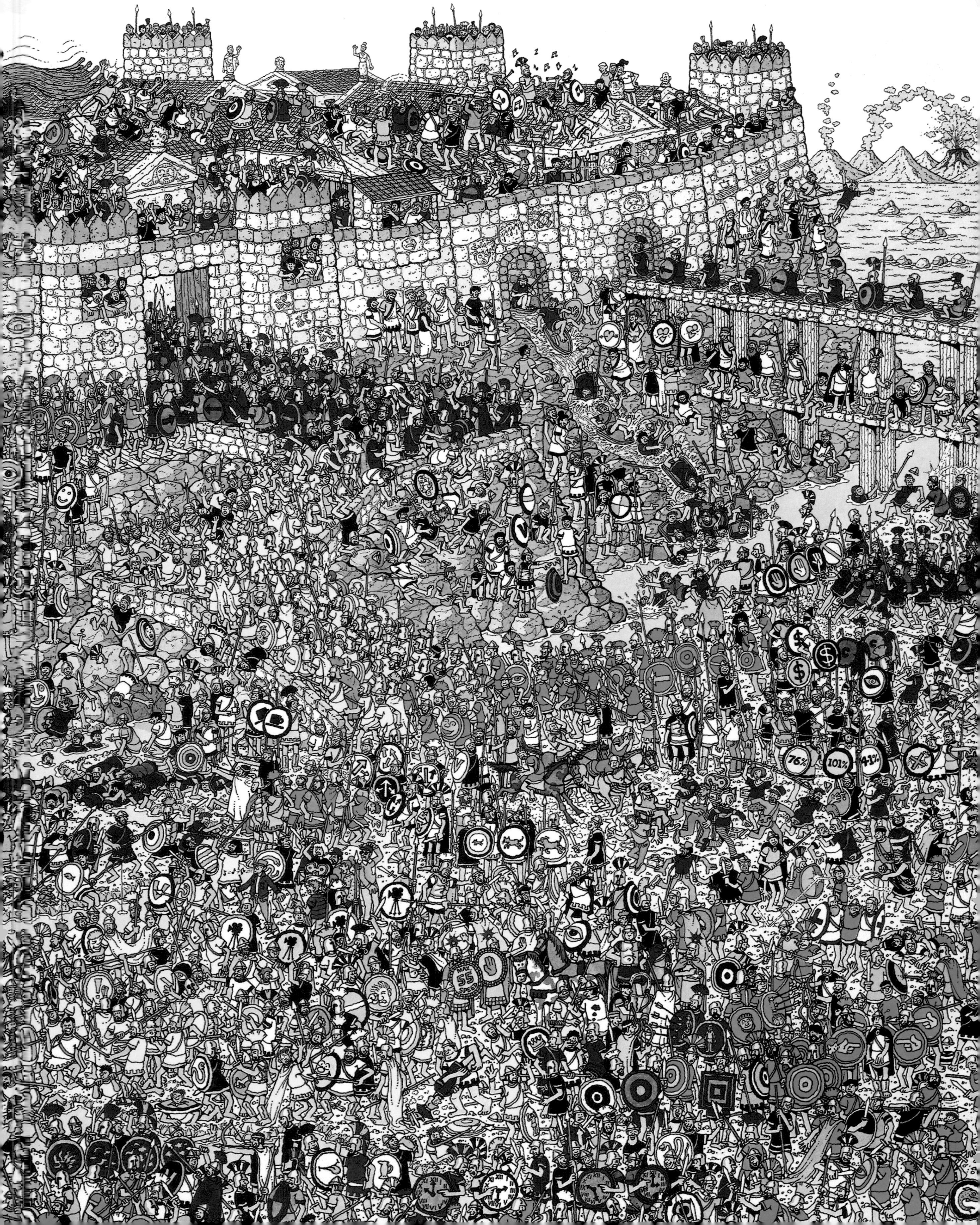
76%
101%

FUN IN THE FOREIGN LEGION

PHEW, FILM FANS, DON'T GET OVERHEATED, THIS IS THE MOST SIZZLING LOCATION SO FAR! EVERYONE'S SWELTERING, FROM STARS TO SAND-SHIFTERS. SOME OF THOSE EXTRAS LOOK LIKE THEY'RE LOSING THEIR COOL — HAVE THEY FORGOTTEN THIS IS ONLY A FILM? PERHAPS IT'S TIME A FEW MORE OF THEM DESERTED THE DESERT AND JOINED THE RUSH FOR ICE-CREAM!

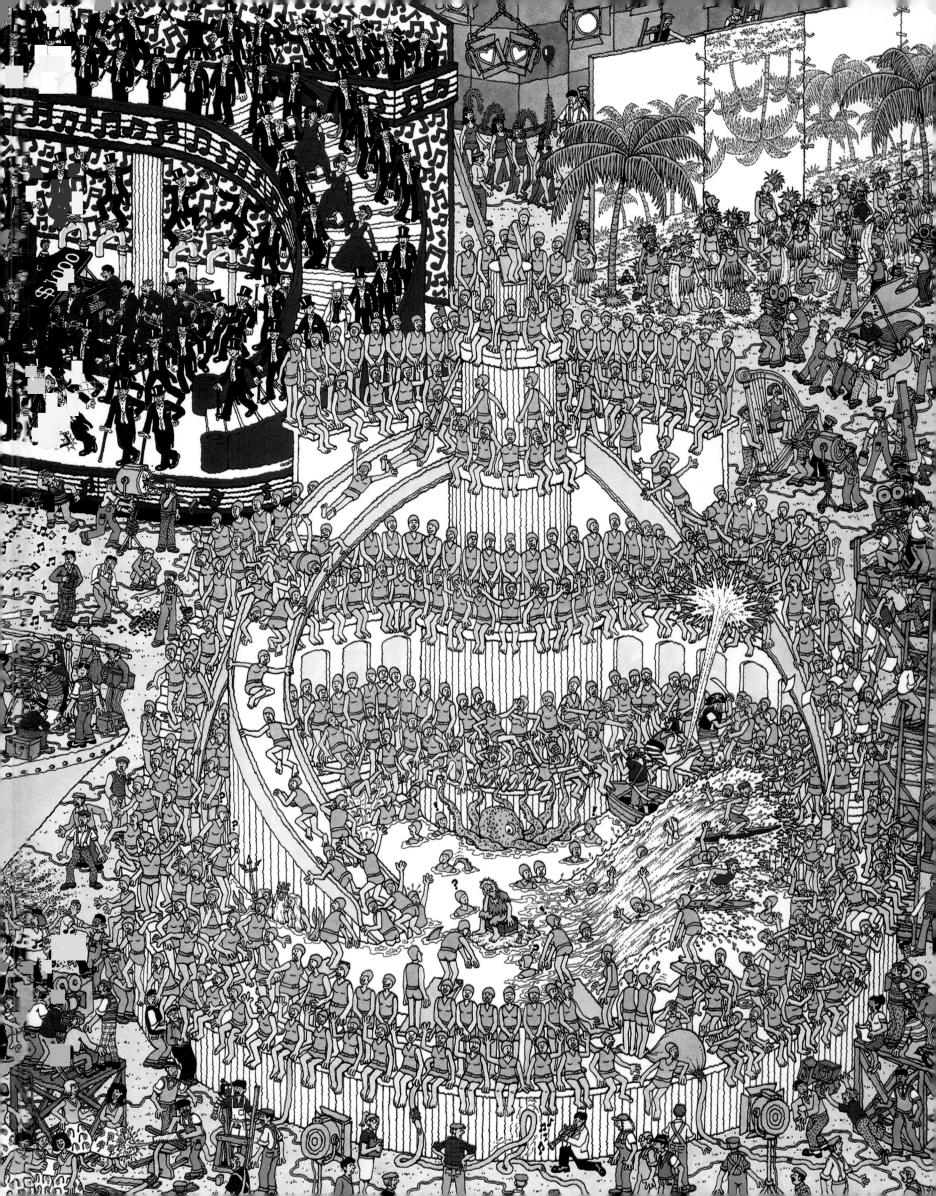

THE SWASHBUCKLING MUSKETEERS

ALL FOR ONE, ONE FOR ALL! – WASN'T THAT THE MOTTO OF THE THREE MUSKETEERS? NOW LOOK AT THIS FREE-FOR-ALL! CAN YOU SPOT OUR THREE GALLANT HEROES BATTLING WITH THE RED-COATED CARDINAL'S GUARDS? WITH ALL THIS SWASHBUCKLING ACTION GOING ON, I WONDER HOW THE CAMERAMEN CAN CAPTURE IT ALL ON FILM!

DINOSAURS, SPACEMEN AND GHOULS

PHEW, INCREDIBLE! TIME, SPACE AND HORROR ARE IN A MIGHTY MUDDLE HERE! WHAT COSMIC COSTUMES AND WHAT GREAT SPECIAL EFFECTS! ONE OF THOSE FLYING SAUCERS LOOKS LIKE IT'S REALLY FLYING! ARE THOSE REAL ALIENS INSIDE, NOT ACTORS AT ALL? SO WHAT'S REAL AND WHAT'S MADE UP IN FILMS LIKE THESE?

WHERE'S WALLY? THE MUSICAL

WOW, WHAT AN EXTRAVAGANZA, WALLY-WATCHERS – THIS ALL-SINGING, ALL-DANCING MOVIE IS ALL ABOUT ME AND MY FRIENDS! LOOK HOW MANY ACTORS ARE DRESSED UP AS ME! AND LOOK AT ALL THE WOOFS, WENDAS, WIZARD WHITEBEARDS AND ODLAWS. HAVE YOU NOTICED THAT THE WARDROBE DEPARTMENT HAS MADE MISTAKES WITH SOME OF THE ACTORS' COSTUMES? BUT THAT WON'T HELP YOU FIND THE REAL ME AND MY FOUR FRIENDS IN THIS FILM! I'LL GIVE YOU SOME CLUES. I'M THE WALLY WITH SOMETHING EXTRA FOR WOOF. ALL YOU CAN SEE OF THE REAL WOOF IS HIS TAIL. THE REAL WENDA HAS A CAMERA. THE REAL WIZARD WHITEBEARD IS WEARING A HAT BENT TO THE LEFT. AND THE REAL ODLAW IS HOLDING A WALKING STICK. THERE'S JUST ONE MORE THING. I'VE BEEN FOLLOWED HERE BY ONE CHARACTER FROM EVERY SET I'VE VISITED. SO CAN YOU SPOT ALL ELEVEN OF THEM IN THIS SCENE? AND CAN YOU FIND OUT WHEN EACH CHARACTER FIRST JOINED ME; AND CATCH ALL THEIR APPEARANCES THROUGHOUT MY TRAVELS?

THE FABULOUS WHERE'S WALLY? IN HOLLYWOOD check list

Lots more things for Wally-watchers to look for!

★ ★ ★ ★ A DREAM COME TRUE ★ ★ ★ ★

- A soldier capturing some food
- A double agent in a spy film
- Someone walking tall
- A swing band
- A green star on a yellow ball
- A wind machine blowing out of control
- A romantic scene
- A girl in a swimsuit with a yellow hat
- Eight pieces of heart-shaped film equipment
- Ten studio security guards
- Twenty-one pirates in striped clothing
- Three shields
- Someone who has put their foot in it
- Three people with skis
- A scenic painter
- A man with a red-and-white-spotted tie
- A friendly pirate

★ ★ SHHH! THIS IS A SILENT MOVIE ★ ★ ★

- A watchtower
- Two mobile cameras
- A director with a giant loudhailer
- A searchlight
- A runaway wheel
- Two butterfly catchers
- Thirteen balloons
- A man in plus-four trousers
- Seven loudhailers
- A trail of leaking buckets
- Nine four-legged animals
- Fifteen cameras
- Some flowers being watered
- Three men tripping on some fruit
- A hose cut by an axe
- Four fire chiefs wearing peaked caps
- A railway-track ladder
- Three men wearing red shirts and braces
- Two umbrellas

★ ★ ★ ★ HORSEPLAY IN TROY ★ ★ ★ ★

- Five blue soldiers with red-crested helmets
- One soldier wearing sandals
- Thirteen real four-legged animals
- Some ancient traffic police
- Five red soldiers with blue-crested helmets
- Two soldiers with slings
- Four first aid soldiers
- Five yellow soldiers with blue-crested helmets
- Five soldiers with brooms
- One soldier with a square shield
- Three film crew members wearing sunglasses
- Three soldiers with extra-long cloaks
- Two statues waving at each other
- Three Trojans drinking coffee
- Ten arrows that are stuck in shields
- A litter bin
- Soldiers arguing about the time

★ ★ ★ FUN IN THE FOREIGN LEGION ★ ★ ★

- Some date trees
- Twelve camels
- A modern aeroplane ruining a camera shot
- Four trees surrendering
- A rock hitting sixteen people
- Two men being shaken out of a tree
- The right costumes in the wrong colours
- A horseman riding in the wrong direction
- A French flag with colours in the wrong order
- Five men wearing vests and shorts
- Some enemies fighting back to back
- An unpopular musician
- A man reading a newspaper
- Three men hiding underneath animals
- An animal treading on a man's foot
- A man surrendering to a shovel

★ ★ A TREMENDOUS SONG AND DANCE ★ ★ ★

- One dancer wearing a blue carnation
- Some tap dancers
- A grand piano
- A musician playing a double bass
- Dancers wearing top hat and tails
- Sailors saluting the ship's "N" sign
- The captain's log
- Sailors with bell-bottom trousers
- A vice admiral
- A piano keyboard
- Four orange feathers
- A soldier on the wrong set
- Five real anchors
- Three watery creatures
- Nine mops
- Four sailors with tattoos

★ ★ ALI BABA AND THE FORTY THIEVES ★ ★ ★

- A man asleep in bed
- Another man awake in bed
- Five animals
- A man wearing yellow shoes
- A man wearing green shoes
- A man wearing a red shoe and a white shoe
- A man wearing a red shoe and a pink shoe
- A chest of drawers
- A man with jewels in his beard
- Two careless carpet carriers
- A man wearing a green turban
- A man wearing a yellow turban
- Four real genies
- A man carrying a grey treasure chest
- A man with a red star on his turban
- A man with a yellow tassel on his fez
- A man with a green tassel on his fez

★ ★ ★ ★ THE WILD, WILD WEST ★ ★ ★ ★

- Two cowboys about to draw against each other
- Drinkers raising their glasses to a lady
- Outlaws holding up a stagecoach
- Some boisterous cowboys painting the town red
- Doc holiday
- The film wardrobe department
- Buffalo Bill
- The loan ranger
- Gamblers playing cards
- A couple of gunslingers
- Calamity Jane
- A buffalo **stamp**ede
- A spaghetti western
- A horse drawn wagon
- Billy the kid
- Townspeople saluting General Store
- A band of outlaws
- Two cowboys shouting, "This town ain't big enough for the both of us."

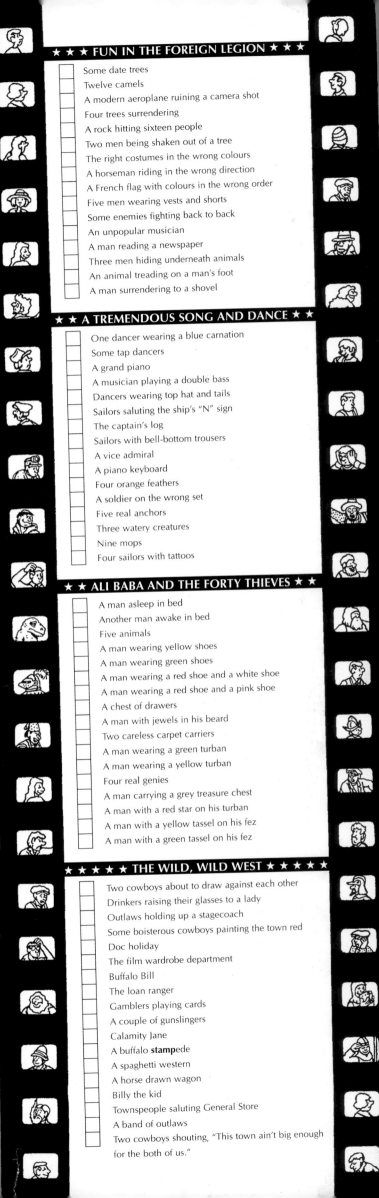

★ ★ THE SWASHBUCKLING MUSKETEERS ★ ★

- Eleven gentlemen bowing
- Two wheelbarrows
- Twelve spouts of water
- A tear-jerking emotional scene
- A gentleman with only one glove
- Three musket tears
- One lost glove
- A man wearing different coloured gloves
- A hat with a striped plume
- Badly dressed men turned away from the dance
- A bouncer
- Three angry gardeners
- Two swordsmen fencing
- Three mixed-up statues
- A man having his foot tickled
- Four ladies being presented with flowers
- Four real animals

★ DINOSAURS, SPACEMEN AND GHOULS ★

- "Hand" luggage
- A fly in saucer
- A ticklish dinosaur
- A greedy green alien
- A dozing dinosaur
- A spaceship
- A cheeky dinosaur
- Stars in a star's dressing room
- A wolfman having a howling good time
- Eight characters in craters
- A planet picnic
- A game of hoopla
- A spacecastle
- Two people reading books
- Four cavemen going up in the world
- An astronaut without helmet, gloves or boots
- Two bottles of ketchup

★ ★ ROBIN HOOD'S MERRY MESS-UP ★ ★

- Eight ladies in medieval costume
- "Little" John leading some men
- Sixteen flags
- Two archers with long bows
- "Maid" Marian tidying up
- A medieval extra with a radio
- A sheriff's soldier with rolled-up sleeves
- "Frier" Tuck
- A night in armour
- A knight with a pink plume in his helmet
- The Sheriff of Nottingham
- A man with a bow and arrow
- A soldier with a large shield
- Medieval soldiers wearing the wrong trousers
- A prisoner with a giant ball and chain
- Five real four-legged animals
- Twenty-one ladders
- Seven helmets with animal crests

★ ★ ★ WHEN THE STARS COME OUT ★ ★ ★

- Twenty-nine lights
- Two rival news reporters
- Someone who has it all wrapped up
- A policeman wanting an autograph
- Three cowboys
- Ten hearts
- Seven large palms
- Someone with a bird's-eye view
- A celebrity wearing a new dress
- Someone making their mark
- Two astronauts
- A sleepy spectator with an alarm clock
- A twisting telescope
- An extra-long straw
- Four celebrities wearing sunglasses

★ ★ ★ WHERE'S WALLY? THE MUSICAL ★ ★ ★

- A Wally jumper with stripes in reverse order
- A Wally with blond hair
- A Wally with a beard
- A Wenda without any shoes
- A Wally wearing shades
- An Odlaw without a moustache
- A Wally jumper with extra stripes
- A haredresser
- A Wally wearing a hat without a bobble
- A Wally without pockets on his jeans
- A Wizard Whitebeard wearing glasses
- A Wally script reading
- A sound mixer
- A Wenda with a blue-and-white-striped umbrella
- A walking stick
- Two Wizard Whitebeards without beards
- A Wally without glasses
- An Odlaw wearing a hat without a bobble
- A Wenda with blonde hair
- A Wally wearing a bobble hat in reverse colours
- A Wenda without glasses
- A Wizard Whitebeard wearing a red hat
- A Woof wearing a bobble hat in reverse colours
- A Wenda wearing round Wally glasses
- A Wally tickling another Wally
- A Woof without a bobble hat
- A Wenda with no pockets on her skirt
- A Wally holding a walking stick the wrong way up
- A Woof wearing a hat without a bobble
- A Woof wearing shades
- A back view of a Wenda
- A Wally in blue and white stripes
- A Wenda who is not wearing a bobble hat
- An Odlaw without shades
- A Wizard Whitebeard dancing
- A back view of a Wally
- A Wizard Whitebeard wearing a bobble hat
- A Woof wearing a blue and white bobble hat
- Two Wizard Whitebeards without white beards
- A Wenda wearing a hat without a bobble
- A Wally with two bobble hats

★ ★ ★ ★ BACK TO THE BEGINNING ★ ★ ★ ★

Did you find Wally, all his friends, and all the things they lost? Did you find the mystery character who appears in every scene except the last? And one more thing: somewhere one of the Wally-watchers lost the bobble from his hat. Can you spot which one, and find the bobble?

Don't go away! The game's not over yet! Go right back to the beginning and look closely at the golden Wally trophies! Ten of them are different from the rest – can you tell which ones?

★ ★ ★ ★ ★ THE FINAL FILM TEST ★ ★ ★ ★ ★

Nearly all the faces in the sprocket holes on this and the facing page appear in colour somewhere else in the book. Can you find where? But … ten of them do *not* appear anywhere else! Can you tell which ten? Lastly … some faces appear more than once in the sprocket holes. Can you see which ones, and how many times each one appears?

WHERE'S WALLY?
IN
HOLLYWOOD

THE END

WHERE'S WALLY?

Have you found all seven Wally books yet?

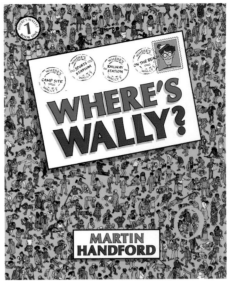

Down the road, over the sea, around the globe… Where's Wally? on his worldwide adventures! Terrific!

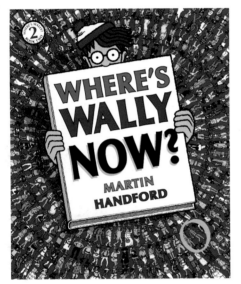

Over thousands of years, past thousands of people… Where's Wally? *now*! Amazing!

Once upon a mermaid, once upon a dragon… Where's Wally? in the realms of fantasy! Magic!

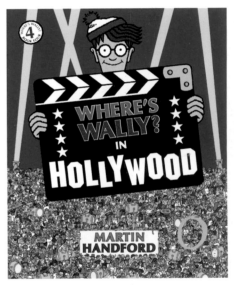

Lights, camera, action... Where's Wally? behind the scenes! Cool!

Stepping off the pages, and into life... Where's Wally? in lands full of wonder! Wow!

Spot the difference, match the silhouettes… Where's Wally? at the gallery! Brilliant!

Press-out board game and circus, a tiny sheet of paper… Where's Wally? amongst all the fun! Super!